Carol Vorderman

Maths
Made Easy
ExtraTests

Author and consultant Sean McArdle

Key Stage 1

AGES
6-7

D0178791

LONDON, NEW YORK, MUNICH, MELBOURNE, and DELHI

DK UK
Senior Editor Deborah Lock
Art Director Martin Wilson
Publishing Director Sophie Mitchell
Pre-production Francesca Wardell
Jacket Designer Martin Wilson
Maths Consultant Sean McArdle

DK Delhi
Editorial Monica Saigal, Tanya Desai
Design Pallavi Narain, Dheeraj Arora,
Tanvi Nathyal, Jyotsna Khosla
DTP Designer Anita Yadav

First published in Great Britain by
Dorling Kindersley Limited
80 Strand, London, WC2R 0RL

A CIP catalogue record for this book
is available from the British Library
ISBN: 978-1-4093-2361-7

Printed and bound in China by L Rex Printing Co., Ltd.

All images © Dorling Kindersley
For further information see: www.dkimages.com

Discover more at
www.dk.com

Contents

This chart lists all the topics in the book. Once you have completed each page, stick a star in the correct box below.

Page	Topic	Star
4	Read, write, and draw	☆
5	Place value	☆
6	Forwards and backwards	☆
7	Counting in 3s and 4s	☆
8	Ordering	☆
9	Sequences	☆
10	Odd or even	☆
11	Using symbols	☆

Page	Topic	Star	Page	Topic	Star
12	Keeping skills sharp	☆	23	Keeping skills sharp	☆
13	Keeping skills sharp	☆	24	Time problems	☆
14	Number families	☆	25	Carroll diagrams	☆
15	Adding up	☆	26	Symmetry	☆
16	Making 20	☆	27	2-D shapes	☆
17	Subtraction	☆	28	3-D shapes	☆
18	Real-life problems	☆	29	Measurement problems	☆
19	Money	☆	30	Keeping skills sharp	☆
20	Doubles	☆	31	Keeping skills sharp	☆
21	Fractions of shapes	☆	32	Certificate	☆
22	Keeping skills sharp	☆	33	Answer section with parents' notes	

Draw each number using the example provided.

Tens	Units
1	9

19

Tens	Units
10	3

27

Tens	Units

38

Hundreds	Tens	Units
100	20	7

127

Hundreds	Tens	Units

105

Write each number as a word.

12 _twelve_   100 _____

31 thirtyone   150 _____

53 fiftythree   165 _____

64 sixty four   173 _____

97 nintyseven   180 _____

How many units are in each number?

12 [2]   25 [ ]   37 [ ]   29 [ ]

106 [6]   117 [ ]   123 [ ]   140 [ ]

How many tens are in each number?

43 [ ]   18 [ ]   59 [ ]   62 [ ]

7 [ ]   96 [ ]   71 [ ]   84 [ ]

What is the place value of 6 in each number?

16 [ ]   62 [ ]   60 [ ]

463 [ ]   46 [ ]   6 [ ]

48 can be written as 40 + 8.
Write each number in this form.

61 [ ]   85 [ ]   42 [ ]

120 [ ]   175 [ ]   191 [ ]

20 + 5 can be written as 25.
Write each number in this form.

10 + 4 [ ]   10 + 7 [ ]   10 + 9 [ ]

20 + 3 [ ]   30 + 8 [ ]   40 + 1 [ ]

100 + 10 [ ]   100 + 40 + 1 [ ]   100 + 50 + 4 [ ]

Count forwards in 2s, 5s, and 10s.

23 26 28 2d 22 24 26

30

36

Count backwards in 2s, 5s, and 10s.

69

46

100

Count forwards in 3s and 4s.

Count backwards in 3s and 4s.

Write the answer.

Which number is 4 less than 62?

Which number is 3 more than 78?

★ Ordering

Write each group of numbers in order, starting with the smallest number.

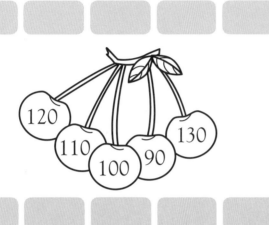

18				

Write each group of numbers in order, starting with the largest number.

Apples bowl: 50, 27, 21, 71, 34

Apples bowl: 50, 5, 500, 55, 550

Add each row after putting the numbers in order, starting from the smallest number.

5   20   3   [ ] + [ ] + [ ] = [ ]

4   10   2   [ ] + [ ] + [ ] = [ ]

30   1   7   [ ] + [ ] + [ ] = [ ]

Write the next five numbers in each row.

12 15 18 21

9 13 17

What numbers are missing in each sequence?

4 16

8 26 29

What numbers are missing in each sequence?

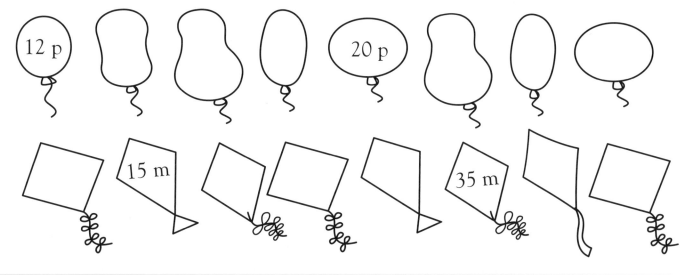

12 p 20 p

15 m 35 m

Circle the numbers that are even.

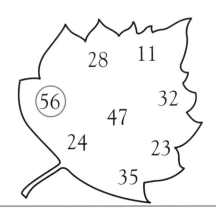

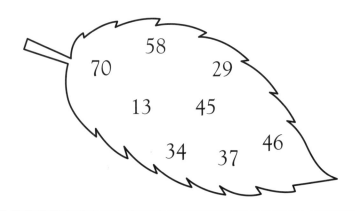

Circle the numbers that are odd.

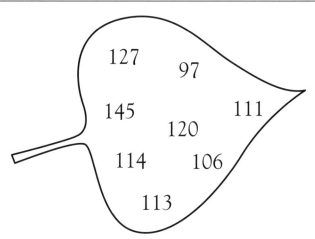

Write the answers.

4 + 2 = 6   6 + 2 = ▢

2 + 0 = ▢   4 + 0 = ▢

3 + 1 = ▢   5 + 3 = ▢

Are your answers odd
or even?   ....

Write the answers.

4 + 3 = ▢   6 + 1 = ▢

8 + 3 = ▢   5 + 2 = ▢

3 + 2 = ▢   7 + 4 = ▢

Are your answers odd
or even?   ....

What happens when you add
two even numbers?   ....

What happens when you add
two odd numbers?   ....

< \ less than	10> 8 greater than	10 = 10 equal to or the same as

Fill in the box with a symbol from above.

861 < 890   423 > 342   678 < 679

209 = 209   299 > 298   323 < 232

999 > 888   802 < 820   300 = 300

one hundred and twelve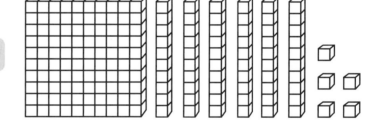

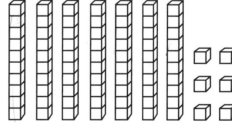

356 =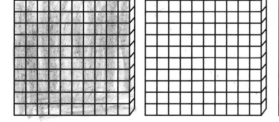

122 =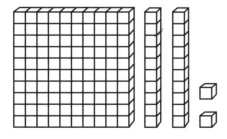

Clara spends 10 p a day on sweets. Clara has 60 p.
How many days will Clara's money last?

....

David gives money to an animal charity. Bill says
he will give £5 more than David.
This is what David gives to charity.
January - £10   February - £18   March - £16
How much does Bill give?

January [ ]   February [ ]   March [ ]

Cala arranges her brothers and sisters in order of size.

Amir   Habib   Nima   Yasir   Jamila
86 cm   140 cm   112 cm   173 cm   97 cm

Write the children's names in order of height, starting with the shortest.

....

In a competition, only the odd numbers win a prize.
Circle which children won.

 39
Bill

 46
Bob

 511
Dave

 208
Ann

 203
Taylor

 122
Ann

345
Barbara

140
Mary

 87
Harris

Write these numbers in words.

45 ....

324 ....

98 ....

176 ....

204 ....

Write these numbers in hundreds + tens + units.

79 [   ]   99 [   ]   378 [   ]

603 [   ]   555 [   ]   241 [   ]

How many tens are in each number?

784 [   ]   54 [   ]   222 [   ]   304 [   ]   98 [   ]

Fill in the box with the right symbol: <, >, or =.

243 [<]

875 [> <] four hundred and ninety seven

998 [<] 999

2 + 2 = 4 and 3 + 1 = 4

Write another way to make 4.

[   ] = 4

4 + 3 = 7 and 6 + 1 = 7

Write another way to make 7.

[   ] = 7

10 + 0 = 10 and 9 + 1 = 10

Write four other ways to make 10.

[   ] = 10   [   ] = 10   [   ] = 10   [   ] = 10

6 − 1 = 5 and 5 − 0 = 5

Write four other ways to make 5.

[   ] = 5   [   ] = 5   [   ] = 5   [   ] = 5

Use the 3 numbers to make 2 addition and 2 subtraction problems.

10   4   6

[6 + 4 = 10]   [4 + 6 = 10]   [10 − 4 = 6]   [10 − 6 = 4]

12   7   5

[   ]   [   ]   [   ]   [   ]

20   13   7

[   ]   [   ]   [   ]   [   ]

15   10   5

[   ]   [   ]   [   ]   [   ]

Adding up

Find the total.

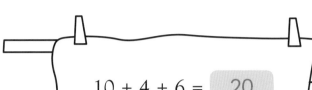

10 + 4 + 6 = 20

12 + 2 + 5 =

12 + 4 + 2 =

20 + 4 + 6 =

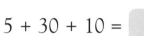

5 + 30 + 10 =

20 + 22 + 5 =

14 + 7 + 5 =

18 + 10 + 3 =

What number is missing?

16 + [ ] = 25

[ ] + 9 = 17

23 + [ ] = 30

[ ] + 14 = 22

Find the sum.

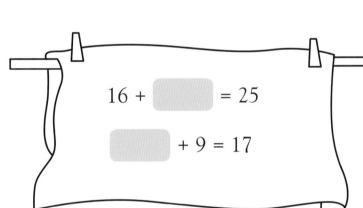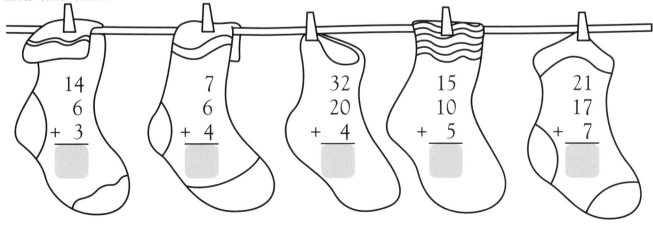

14	7	32	15	21
6	6	20	10	17
+ 3	+ 4	+ 4	+ 5	+ 7

All the answers are 20!

Find the missing numbers.

18 + [2] = 20   10 + [   ] = 20   15 + [   ] = 20

19 + [   ] = 20   12 + [   ] = 20   5 + [   ] = 20

30 − [   ] = 20   40 − [   ] = 20   50 − [   ] = 20

28 − [   ] = 20   31 − [   ] = 20   45 − [   ] = 20

6 + 5 + [   ] = 20   10 + 3 + [   ] = 20   14 + 2 + [   ] = 20

4 + 5 + [   ] = 20   8 + 3 + [   ] = 20   1 + 2 + [   ] = 20

[   ] + 9 = 20   [   ] + 4 = 20   [   ] + 17 = 20

32 − [   ] = 20   38 − [   ] = 20   100 − [   ] = 20

Use the 3 numbers to make 20.

12   5   3   [12 + 5 + 3 = 20]

34   8   6   [   ]

15   10   5   [   ]

42   32   10   [   ]

Take 5 away from each group. How many are left?

2

6

Take 7 away from each group. How many are left?

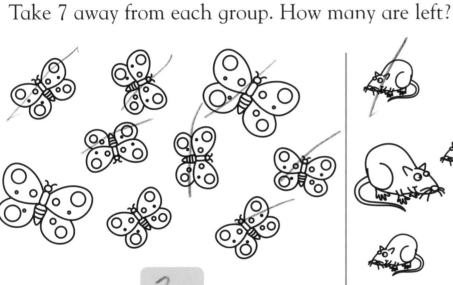

2

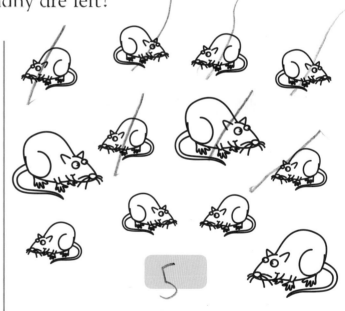

5

Write the answers.

$12 - 7 =$ ⬚ $15 - 5 =$ ⬚ $18 - 6 =$ ⬚

$14 - 9 =$ ⬚ $20 - 4 =$ ⬚ $17 - 8 =$ ⬚

$43 - 3 =$ ⬚ $57 - 6 =$ ⬚ $64 - 12 =$ ⬚

Abe has a packet of 12 biscuits.
Martha eats 5 biscuits.

How many biscuits does Abe have left?

7

Jake puts £20 into a charity box.
Charlie puts double that amount
in the charity box.

How much have Jake and Charlie
put in together?

Mary has 6 boxes of oranges.
Each box has 10 oranges.

How many oranges does Mary have altogether?

50012

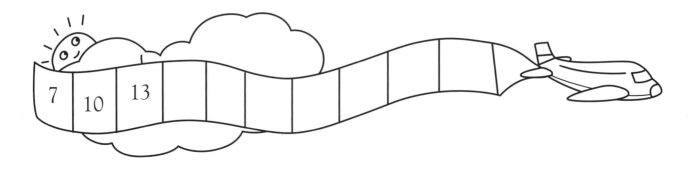

Complete the sequence.

7 10 13

What coin is missing?

= 15 p

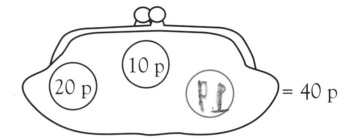
= 40 p

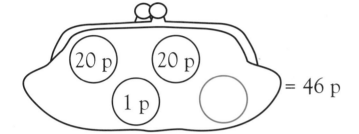
= 46 p

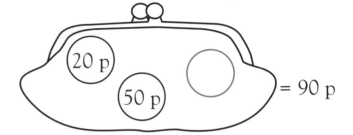
= 90 p

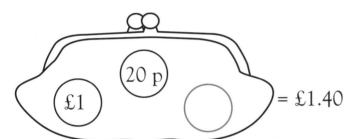
= £1.40

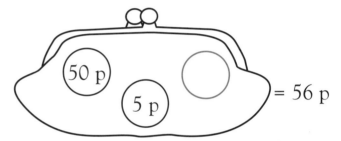
= 56 p

Write three different ways of making 15 p using 1 p and 5 p coins only.	Write four different ways of making 25 p using 1 p, 5 p, and 10 p only.

Sahid has these coins. How much more does Sahid need to have £1?

    (5 p) ( ) = £1

What is double each number?

    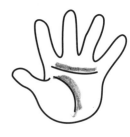

| 2 | 4 | 6 | 8 | 10 |

| 2 p | 6 p | 10 p | 8 cm | 12 g |

Write the answers.

8 + 8 =   double 8 is    2 groups of 8 are

9 + 9 =   double 9 is   two nines are 18

double 12 is   15 + 15 =   double 20 is

Write the missing number.

8 + 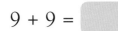 = 16   9 + = 18   10 + = 20

7 + = 14   + 6 = 12   + 11 = 22

+ 20 = 40   + 0 = 0   + 13 = 26

Fractions of shapes

Colour half ($\frac{1}{2}$) of the squares.

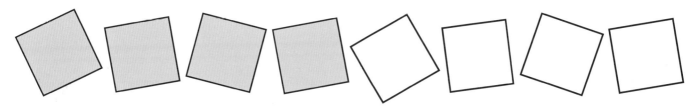

Colour a quarter ($\frac{1}{4}$) of the triangles.

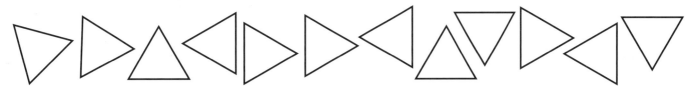

Colour one-third ($\frac{1}{3}$) of the circles.

Colour one-third ($\frac{1}{3}$) of the pentagons.

Label the parts of each shape.

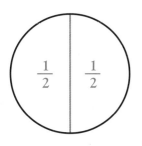

$\frac{1}{2}$ $\frac{1}{2}$

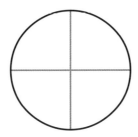

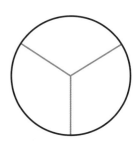

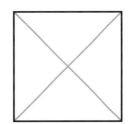

Gerard can make 8 by adding 5 and 3. Make 8
by adding in different ways than Gerard.

[   ] = 8   [   ] = 8   [   ] = 8   [   ] = 8

Add these amounts.	Fill in the missing number.
20 p + 10 p = [ ]	8 + [ ] = 15
35 p + 40 p = [ ]	5 + [ ] = 15
5 p + 4 p + 3 p = [ ]	21 – [ ] = 15
18 p + 6 p + 10 p = [ ]	30 – [ ] = 15

Each child gives 6 grapes to a friend. They start with these numbers.

Erik	Mirka	Pawel	Krysta
20	17	24	11

How many grapes do they have left when they give 6 away?

[   ]   [   ]   [   ]   [   ]

Write the answers.

$$35 - 9 = \boxed{}$$ $$41 - 20 = \boxed{}$$ $$57 - 8 = \boxed{}$$ $$74 - 22 = \boxed{}$$ $$94 - 7 = \boxed{}$$

Dan has eight boxes. Each box holds four toys. How many toys does Dan have all together?

How much does Emmie have all together?

Jim thinks of a number.

He doubles the number.

He doubles the number again!

His answer is 20.

What number did Jim start with?

Julie went to the shop and received £0.46 in change. Write three different sets of coins she could have received.

Find the answers.

Two sixes are 12   5 + 5 + 5 = 25   3 + 3 + 3 + 3 =

How many minutes are between these times in the morning?

....

....

The time in the morning is shown on this clock. Ahmed is looking forward to lunch at noon. How long does Ahmed have to wait until lunch?

2 hours
....

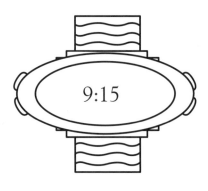

This is Maggie's watch. It is 15 minutes slow. What is the actual time?

....

This is Max's clock. It is half an hour fast. What is the actual time?

....

This is the time shown on Ann's watch. Ann's bus arrives at 11.00. How many minutes must Ann wait for her bus?

....

15 numbers were put into this diagram. Look at the diagram.

Tuking away	Odd numbers	Even numbers
Less than 20	5, 9, 15, 17	2, 8, 16, 18
More than 20	21, 35, 47, 59	22, 26, 30

How many numbers are odd? | 8 |

How many numbers are even? | |

Which numbers are even and less than 20? | |

Which numbers are odd and more than 20? | |

How many numbers larger than 20 but not even are shown? | |

Look at the diagram.

	Countries	Animals
Africa	Egypt, South Africa, Libya	Lion, Hippo, Zebra
America	USA, Mexico, Canada, Brazil	Rattlesnake, Bison, Grizzly bear

How many African countries are named? ....

Are any American animals in the African list? ....

How many different animals are named? ....

Which animals are not from America? ....

Which animals are not from Africa? ....

Draw a line of symmetry on each shape.

Complete each shape.

Draw lines of symmetry on these shapes. Use a mirror if it helps.

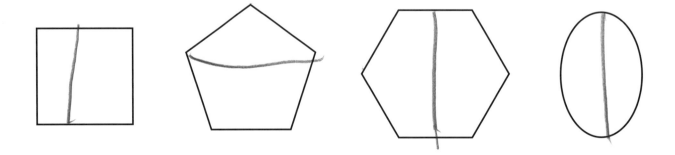

Look at these shapes. Fill in the details.

Name of shape .... square ....

Number of sides   4

Number of corners   4

Name of shape 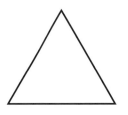 triangle

Number of sides   3 three

Number of corners   3 three

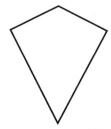

Name of shape ...DinanD...

Number of sides

Number of corners

Name of shape 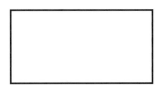 ...rectangle

Number of sides   4

Number of corners   4

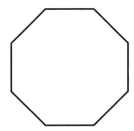

Name of shape ...hexogan...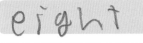

Number of sides   eight

Number of corners   8

Name of shape 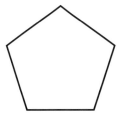 pentogan

Number of sides   5 five

Number of corners   fives 5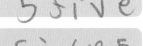

Look at the shapes. Fill in the details.

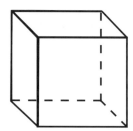

Name of shape .... cube ....

Number of edges   12

Number of vertices (corners)   8

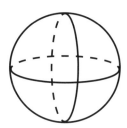

Name of shape ....

Number of edges

Number of vertices (corners)

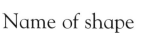

Name of shape ....

Number of edges

Number of vertices (corners)

Name of shape ....

Number of edges

Number of vertices (corners)

Name of shape ....

Number of edges

Number of vertices (corners)

Name of shape ....

Number of edges

Number of vertices (corners)

Amy wants to measure the length of her bed using a 30-cm ruler. About how many rulers-long do you think Amy's bed will be?

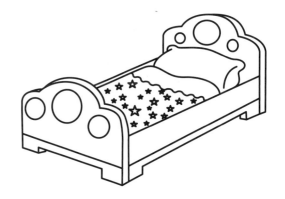

....

This measuring jug holds 1 litre of water. How many jugs will be needed to fill a bowl that can take 5 litres?

....

Pat has to measure the length of the garden. Circle the best item to use.

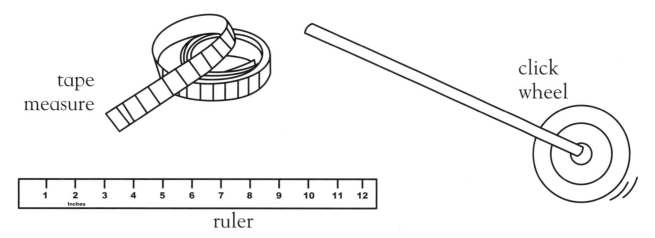

tape measure

ruler

click wheel

One apple weighs about 200 g.

Estimate how much two apples will weigh.

Estimate how much three apples will weigh.

Jenny is going to a party at 5 o'clock.
This is the time now. How many
minutes must Jenny wait? ....

Put these numbers in the correct place.

8   12   14   9   4   18   21

	Odd numbers	Even numbers
Less than 10		
More than 10		

Look at this table.

	Class 3	Class 4	Class 5	Class 6
Boys	15	16	12	14
Girls	16	14	17	17

Which two classes have the same number of children? ....

In how many classes are there more girls than boys? ....

Complete this picture to make the house symmetric.

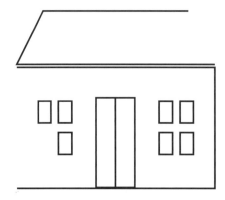

Look at these shapes.

  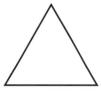 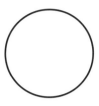

Danni says all the shapes have straight sides. Is she right? ....

Fiona says the shapes all have four angles. Is she right? ....

Look at these shapes. Name each shape.

  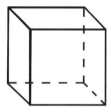

....

Which shape has no curved faces?   ....

Which shape has only two flat faces?   ....

Which unit of measurement is correct
for the height of a giraffe?   ....

a. 700 centimetres   b. 700 metres   c. 700 kilometres

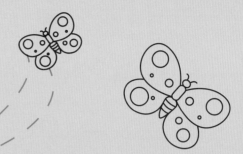

Certificate

Ages 6-7

Congratulations to

eLyer

for successfully

finishing this book.

WELL DONE!

You're a star.

★★★★★

Date

30.1.19

Answer Section
with Parents' Notes

This book is intended to help extend young children's understanding of mathematics. The maths covered will be very similar to the work they encounter in the second year of primary school.

Contents
By working through this book, your child will practise:
- understanding place value of hundreds, tens, and units;
- building fluency with addition and subtraction;
- the concept of number families;
- understanding of odd and even numbers;
- solving money problems and telling the time;
- using symbols of less than, equal, and greater than;
- continuing simple sequences and patterns;
- recognising the properties of 2-D shapes and 3-D shapes;
- recognising fractions of shapes and objects;
- using units of measurement.

How to help your child
Your child will be increasingly able to read the more specialised maths words ("symmetry", for example), but do be prepared to assist. Working alongside your child also greatly benefits your understanding of how your child is thinking and where the stumbling blocks may be.

As children progress in mathematics, they will have more questions based on real-life problems to solve. They will need to identify what numbers to use and whether to add or subtract at this level. If children really understand the maths, they will be able to reason critically and know what needs to be done.

When appropriate, use props to help your child visualise the solutions – for example, have a collection of coins to use for the money problems, or find examples of objects to measure around your house.

Build your child's confidence with words of praise. If they are getting answers wrong, encourage them to try again another time.
Good luck and remember to have fun.

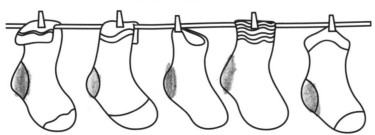

★ Read, write, and draw

Draw each number using the example provided.

Tens	Units	Tens	Units	Tens	Units
1	9	2	7	3	8

19   27   38

Hundreds	Tens	Units	Hundreds	Tens	Units
1	2	7	1	0	5

127   105

Write each number as a word.

12	twelve	100	one hundred
31	thirty one	150	one hundred and fifty
53	fifty three	165	one hundred and sixty five
64	sixty four	173	one hundred and seventy three
97	ninety seven	180	one hundred and eighty

At this age, children may not be able to spell the words correctly but that is not too important. The main thing is they should be able to say the word properly and have a good attempt at a reasonable spelling.

Place value ★

How many units are in each number?

12	2	25	5	37	7	29	9
106	6	117	7	123	3	140	0

How many tens are in each number?

43	4	18	1	59	5	62	6
7	0	96	9	71	7	84	8

What is the place value of 6 in each number?

16	units	62	tens	60	tens
463	tens	46	units	6	units

48 can be written as 40 + 8.
Write each number in this form.

61	60 + 1	85	80 + 5	42	40 + 2
120	100 + 20	175	100 + 70 + 5	191	100 + 90 + 1

20 + 5 can be written as 25.
Write each number in this form.

10 + 4	14	10 + 7	17	10 + 9	19
20 + 3	23	30 + 8	38	40 + 1	41
100 + 10	110	100 + 40 + 1	141	100 + 50 + 4	154

Children should be able to recognise the value of numbers according to their positions. Partitioning is a simple but very useful skill that will help with all sorts of operations in later years.

★ Forwards and backwards

Count forwards in 2s, 5s, and 10s.

23 +2 25 +2 27

50 −2 48 −2 46

Count forwards in 2s, 5s, and 10s.

23 +2 25 27 29 31 33

30 +5 35 40 45 50 55

36 +10 46 56 66 76 86

Count backwards in 2s, 5s, and 10s.

69 −2 67 65 63 61 59

46 −5 41 36 31 26 21

100 −10 90 80 70 60 50

Counting in equal amounts is a useful skill and this work will help with learning multiples of 2, 5, and 10 and will help them next year when they learn their times tables. It will also aid with more general sequence problems.

Counting in 3s and 4s ★

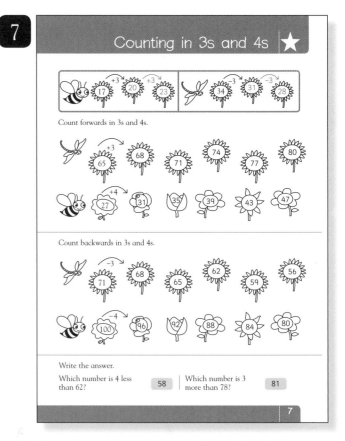

17 +3 20 +3 23

34 −3 31 −3 28

Count forwards in 3s and 4s.

65 +3 68 71 74 77 80

27 +4 31 35 39 43 47

Count backwards in 3s and 4s.

71 −3 68 65 62 59 56

100 −4 96 92 88 84 80

Write the answer.

Which number is 4 less than 62?   58   Which number is 3 more than 78?   81

This page continues to reinforce the idea of "more" and "less". Provide children with a number line if they find these questions tricky.

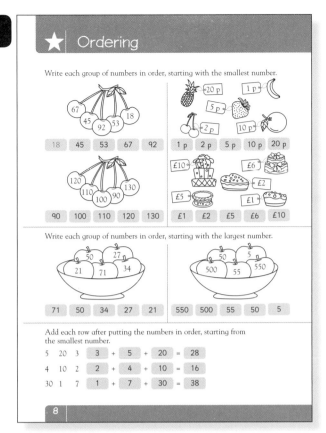

★ Ordering

Write each group of numbers in order, starting with the smallest number.

| 18 | 45 | 53 | 67 | 92 |

| 1 p | 2 p | 5 p | 10 p | 20 p |

| 90 | 100 | 110 | 120 | 130 |

| £1 | £2 | £5 | £6 | £10 |

Write each group of numbers in order, starting with the largest number.

| 71 | 50 | 34 | 27 | 21 |

| 550 | 500 | 55 | 50 | 5 |

Add each row after putting the numbers in order, starting from the smallest number.

5 20 3   **3** + **5** + **20** = **28**

4 10 2   **2** + **4** + **10** = **16**

30 1 7   **1** + **7** + **30** = **38**

Ordering numbers and amounts helps to reinforce basic number understanding and recognition of when something is more or less than another thing.

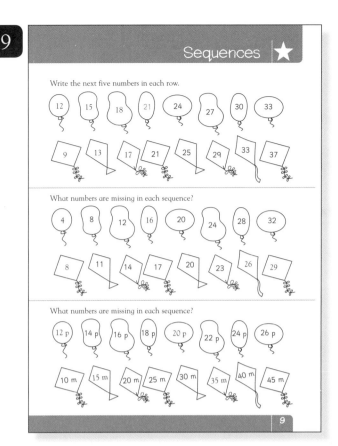

Sequences ★

Write the next five numbers in each row.

12 15 18 21 24 27 30 33

9 13 17 21 25 29 33 37

What numbers are missing in each sequence?

4 8 12 16 20 24 28 32

8 11 14 17 20 23 26 29

What numbers are missing in each sequence?

12 p 14 p 16 p 18 p 20 p 22 p 24 p 26 p

10 m 15 m 20 m 25 m 30 m 35 m 40 m 45 m

The first question is fairly straightforward but the next two will require children to work out for themselves the steps that have been taken.

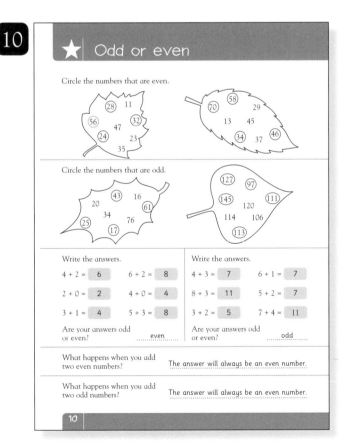

★ Odd or even

Circle the numbers that are even.

28 11
56 32
47
24 23
35

58
70 29
13 45
34 37 46

Circle the numbers that are odd.

43 16
20 61
34
76
25 17

127 97
145 111
120
114 106
113

Write the answers.

4 + 2 = **6**   6 + 2 = **8**

2 + 0 = **2**   4 + 0 = **4**

3 + 1 = **4**   5 + 3 = **8**

Are your answers odd or even? .... even

Write the answers.

4 + 3 = **7**   6 + 1 = **7**

8 + 3 = **11**   5 + 2 = **7**

3 + 2 = **5**   7 + 4 = **11**

Are your answers odd or even? .... odd

What happens when you add two even numbers?   The answer will always be an even number.

What happens when you add two odd numbers?   The answer will always be an even number.

By this age, children should understand that however large a number is, whether it is odd or even can be decided by simply looking at the units.

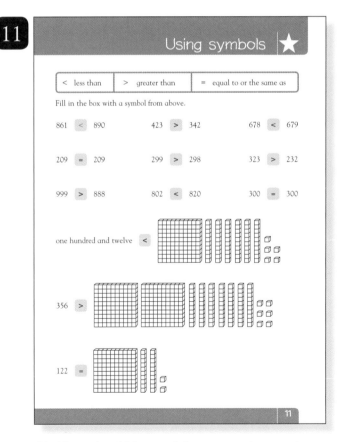

Using symbols ★

| < less than | > greater than | = equal to or the same as |

Fill in the box with a symbol from above.

861 **<** 890   423 **>** 342   678 **<** 679

209 **=** 209   299 **>** 298   323 **>** 232

999 **>** 888   802 **<** 820   300 **=** 300

one hundred and twelve **<**

356 **>**

122 **=**

Children should be confident in reading and recognising numbers that are written as words or digits and in base ten blocks. This activity reinforces their knowledge of comparing numbers, using mathematical symbols.

★ Keeping skills sharp

Clara spends 10 p a day on sweets. Clara has 60 p.
How many days will Clara's money last?   6 days

David gives money to an animal charity. Bill says
he will give £5 more than David.
This is what David gives to charity.
January - £10   February - £18   March - £16
How much does Bill give?

January £15   February £23   March £21

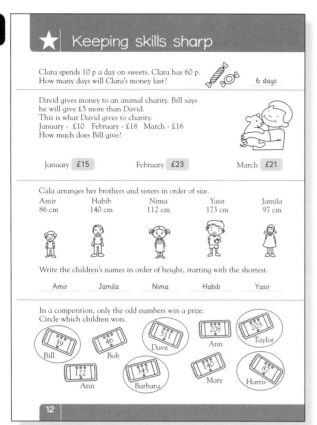

Cala arranges her brothers and sisters in order of size.

Amir	Habib	Nima	Yasir	Jamila
86 cm	140 cm	112 cm	173 cm	97 cm

Write the children's names in order of height, starting with the shortest.

Amir   Jamila   Nima   Habib   Yasir

In a competition, only the odd numbers win a prize.
Circle which children won.

39 Bill   46 Bob   511 Dave   208 Ann   203 Taylor
122 Ann   345 Barbara   140 Mary   87 Harris

This work revises the contents of the previous pages. If the answer to a question is incorrect or proves difficult to reach, revise the appropriate work with some explanation.

Keeping skills sharp ★

Write these numbers in words.

45	forty five
324	three hundred and twenty four
98	ninety eight
176	one hundred and seventy six
204	two hundred and four

Write these numbers in hundreds + tens + units.

| 79 | 70 + 9 | 99 | 90 + 9 | 378 | 300 + 70 + 8 |
| 603 | 600 + 3 | 555 | 500 + 50 + 5 | 241 | 200 + 40 + 1 |

How many tens are in each number?

784 **8**   54 **5**   222 **2**   304 **0**   98 **9**

Fill in the box with the right symbol: <, >, or =.

243 **=** (base ten blocks)

875 **>** four hundred and ninety seven

998 **<** 999

★ Number families

2 + 2 = 4 and 3 + 1 = 4

Write another way to make 4.
Answers may vary.

1 + 3 = 4

4 + 3 = 7 and 6 + 1 = 7

Write another way to make 7.
Answers may vary.

2 + 5 = 7

10 + 0 = 10 and 9 + 1 = 10

Write four other ways to make 10. Answers may vary.

3 + 7 = 10   **2 + 8** = 10   **5 + 5** = 10   **6 + 4** = 10

6 – 1 = 5 and 5 – 0 = 5

Write four other ways to make 5. Answers may vary.

7 – 2 = 5   **8 – 3** = 5   **1 + 4** = 5   **2 + 3** = 5

Use the 3 numbers to make 2 addition and 2 subtraction problems.

10   4   6
6 + 4 = 10   4 + 6 = 10   10 – 4 = 6   10 – 6 = 4

12   7   5
12 – 5 = 7   7 + 5 = 12   12 – 7 = 5   5 + 7 = 12

20   13   7
20 – 13 = 7   20 – 7 = 13   13 + 7 = 20   7 + 13 = 20

15   10   5
15 – 10 = 5   5 + 10 = 15   15 – 5 = 10   10 + 5 = 15

This number-bond practice will help children with calculations and mental agility. They should be able to see how numbers can be connected and manipulated.

Adding up ★

Find the total.

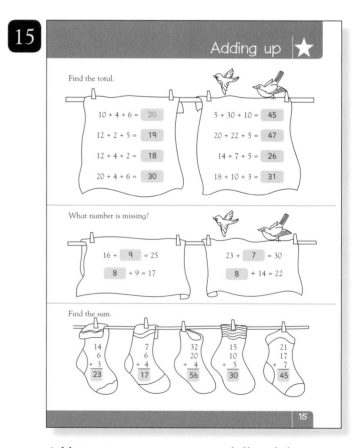

10 + 4 + 6 =	20
12 + 2 + 5 =	19
12 + 4 + 2 =	18
20 + 4 + 6 =	30

5 + 30 + 10 =	45
20 + 22 + 5 =	47
14 + 7 + 5 =	26
18 + 10 + 3 =	31

What number is missing?

16 + **9** = 25   23 + **7** = 30

8 + 9 = 17   **8** + 14 = 22

Find the sum.

14	7	32	15	21
6	6	20	10	17
+ 3	+ 4	+ 4	+ 5	+ 7
23	17	56	30	45

Addition is a most important skill and these questions use slightly different formats to test your child's abilities. Column addition may be taught at a later age in some schools.

★ Making 20

All the answers are 20!

Find the missing numbers.

18 + 2 = 20   10 + 10 = 20   15 + 5 = 20

19 + 1 = 20   12 + 8 = 20   5 + 15 = 20

30 – 10 = 20   40 – 20 = 20   50 – 30 = 20

28 – 8 = 20   31 – 11 = 20   45 – 25 = 20

6 + 5 + 9 = 20   10 + 3 + 7 = 20   14 + 2 + 4 = 20

4 + 5 + 11 = 20   8 + 3 + 9 = 20   1 + 2 + 17 = 20

11 + 9 = 20   16 + 4 = 20   3 + 17 = 20

32 – 12 = 20   38 – 18 = 20   100 – 80 = 20

Use the 3 numbers to make 20.

12   5   3   12 + 5 + 3 = 20

34   8   6   34 – 8 – 6 = 20

15   10   5   15 + 10 – 5 = 20

42   32   10   42 – 32 + 10 = 20

Children's mental agility and simple number knowledge will be tested on this page and they should be becoming more adept at seeing connections between numbers and operations in simple number sentences like these.

Subtraction ★

Take 5 away from each group. How many are left?

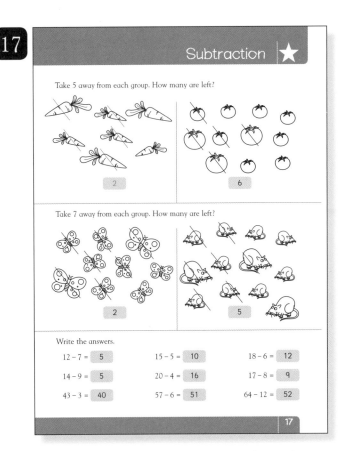

2   6

Take 7 away from each group. How many are left?

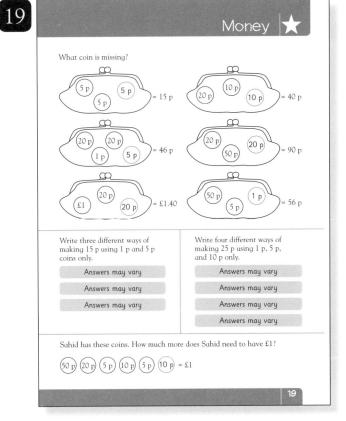

2   5

Write the answers.

12 – 7 = 5   15 – 5 = 10   18 – 6 = 12

14 – 9 = 5   20 – 4 = 16   17 – 8 = 9

43 – 3 = 40   57 – 6 = 51   64 – 12 = 52

Group subtraction is sometimes taught at this age although children may still be reliant on simpler techniques.

★ Real-life problems

Abe has a packet of 12 biscuits.
Martha eats 5 biscuits.

How many biscuits does Abe have left?   7

Jake puts £20 into a charity box.
Charlie puts double that amount
in the charity box.

How much have Jake and Charlie
put in together?   £60

Mary has 6 boxes of oranges.
Each box has 10 oranges.

How many oranges does Mary have altogether?

60

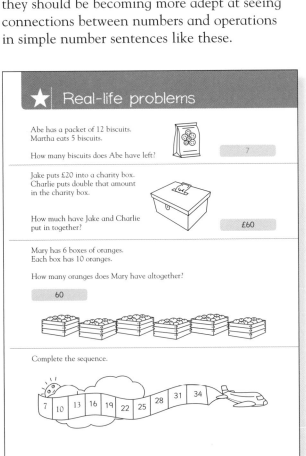

Complete the sequence.

7   10   13   16   19   22   25   28   31   34

It can be difficult for children to sort out what the problem actually is when answers are wrapped up in words. Some teachers use techniques whereby children either underline the important words or use a highlight pen.

Money ★

What coin is missing?

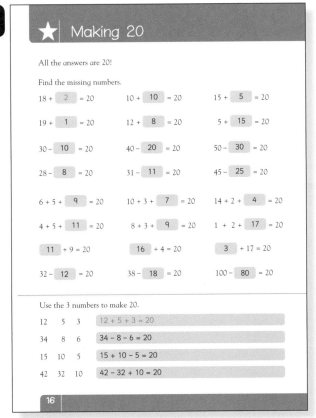

5 p   5 p   5 p = 15 p   20 p   10 p   10 p = 40 p

20 p   20 p   1 p   5 p = 46 p   20 p   50 p   20 p = 90 p

£1   20 p   20 p = £1.40   50 p   5 p   1 p = 56 p

Write three different ways of making 15 p using 1 p and 5 p coins only.

Answers may vary

Answers may vary

Answers may vary

Write four different ways of making 25 p using 1 p, 5 p, and 10 p only.

Answers may vary

Answers may vary

Answers may vary

Answers may vary

Sahid has these coins. How much more does Sahid need to have £1?

50 p   20 p   5 p   10 p   5 p   10 p = £1

The use of actual coins on the table while your child completes these questions will be helpful.

20

★ Doubles

What is double each number?

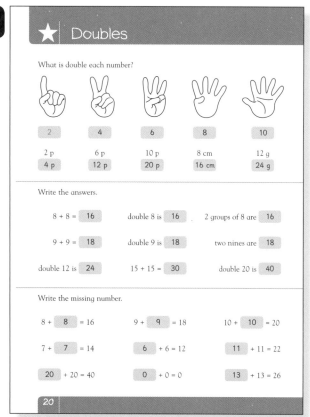

| 2 | 4 | 6 | 8 | 10 |

| 2 p | 6 p | 10 p | 8 cm | 12 g |
| 4 p | 12 p | 20 p | 16 cm | 24 g |

Write the answers.

8 + 8 = 16   double 8 is 16   2 groups of 8 are 16

9 + 9 = 18   double 9 is 18   two nines are 18

double 12 is 24   15 + 15 = 30   double 20 is 40

Write the missing number.

8 + 8 = 16   9 + 9 = 18   10 + 10 = 20

7 + 7 = 14   6 + 6 = 12   11 + 11 = 22

20 + 20 = 40   0 + 0 = 0   13 + 13 = 26

20

Apart from reinforcing work on doubling, this page also reminds children that the same problem can be expressed in many different ways.

21

Fractions of shapes ★

Colour half ($\frac{1}{2}$) of the squares.

Colour a quarter ($\frac{1}{4}$) of the triangles.

Colour one-third ($\frac{1}{3}$) of the circles.

Colour one-third ($\frac{1}{3}$) of the pentagons.

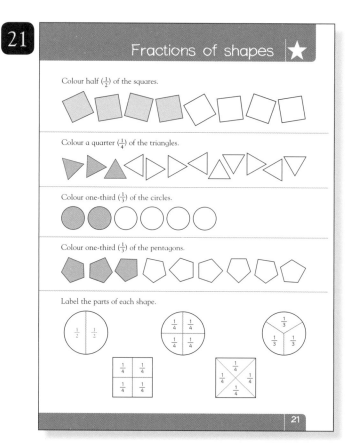

Label the parts of each shape.

21

Thirds are introduced in this work. Recognising that some shapes may be divided in more than one way is important, as with the square divided into quarters by using diagonals.

22

★ Keeping skills sharp

Gerard can make 8 by adding 5 and 3. Make 8 by adding in different ways than Gerard. Answers may vary.

2 + 6 = 8   1 + 7 = 8   4 + 4 = 8   8 + 0 = 8

Add these amounts.	Fill in the missing number.
20 p + 10 p = 30 p	8 + 7 = 15
35 p + 40 p = 75 p	5 + 10 = 15
5 p + 4 p + 3 p = 12 p	21 – 6 = 15
18 p + 6 p + 10 p = 34 p	30 – 15 = 15

Each child gives 6 grapes to a friend. They start with these numbers.

Erik 20   Mirka 17   Pawel 24   Krysta 11

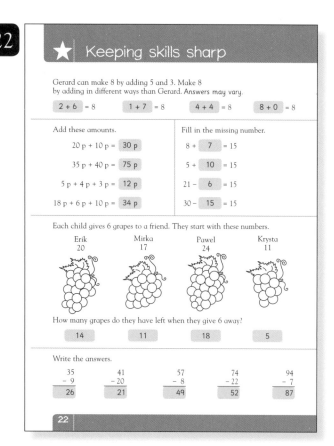

How many grapes do they have left when they give 6 away?

14   11   18   5

Write the answers.

35	41	57	74	94
– 9	– 20	– 8	– 22	– 7
26	21	49	52	87

22

This work revises the contents of the previous pages. If children struggle with a particular question, then revise the appropriate page or pages.

23

Keeping skills sharp ★

Dan has eight boxes. Each box holds four toys. How many toys does Dan have all together?

32

How much does Emmie have all together?

84 p

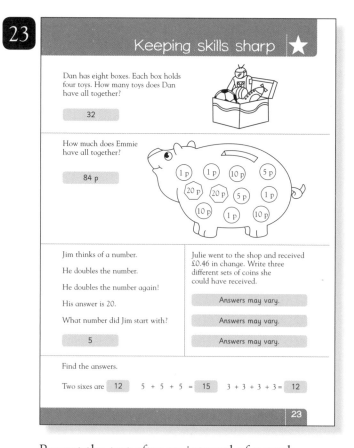

Jim thinks of a number.
He doubles the number.
He doubles the number again!
His answer is 20.
What number did Jim start with?

5

Julie went to the shop and received £0.46 in change. Write three different sets of coins she could have received.

Answers may vary.

Answers may vary.

Answers may vary.

Find the answers.

Two sixes are 12   5 + 5 + 5 = 15   3 + 3 + 3 + 3 = 12

23

Repeat the test after an interval of a week or two to see what progress has been made by your child.

★ Time problems

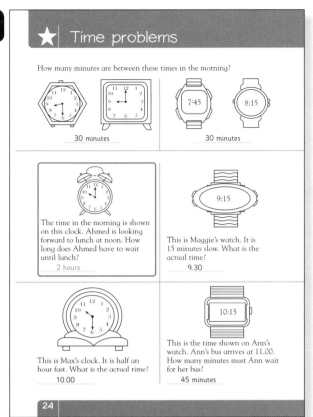

How many minutes are between these times in the morning?

30 minutes

30 minutes

The time in the morning is shown on this clock. Ahmed is looking forward to lunch at noon. How long does Ahmed have to wait until lunch?
2 hours

This is Maggie's watch. It is 15 minutes slow. What is the actual time?
9.30

This is Max's clock. It is half an hour fast. What is the actual time?
10.00

This is the time shown on Ann's watch. Ann's bus arrives at 11.00. How many minutes must Ann wait for her bus?
45 minutes

Knowing how to read various clock displays is important but these questions will help children use the knowledge in practical situations. They should know by this stage that an hour has 60 minutes and a day has 24 hours.

Carroll diagrams ★

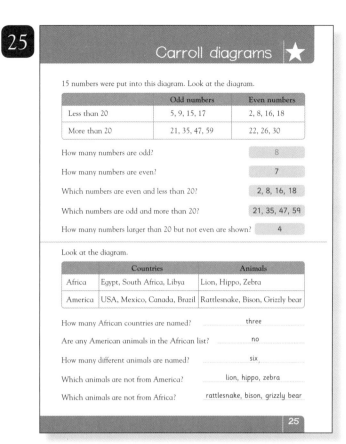

15 numbers were put into this diagram. Look at the diagram.

	Odd numbers	Even numbers
Less than 20	5, 9, 15, 17	2, 8, 16, 18
More than 20	21, 35, 47, 59	22, 26, 30

How many numbers are odd? 8

How many numbers are even? 7

Which numbers are even and less than 20? 2, 8, 16, 18

Which numbers are odd and more than 20? 21, 35, 47, 59

How many numbers larger than 20 but not even are shown? 4

Look at the diagram.

	Countries	Animals
Africa	Egypt, South Africa, Libya	Lion, Hippo, Zebra
America	USA, Mexico, Canada, Brazil	Rattlesnake, Bison, Grizzly bear

How many African countries are named? three

Are any American animals in the African list? no

How many different animals are named? six

Which animals are not from America? lion, hippo, zebra

Which animals are not from Africa? rattlesnake, bison, grizzly bear

Some children can find Carroll diagrams confusing so it may be helpful to sit alongside them while they work on this page.

★ Symmetry

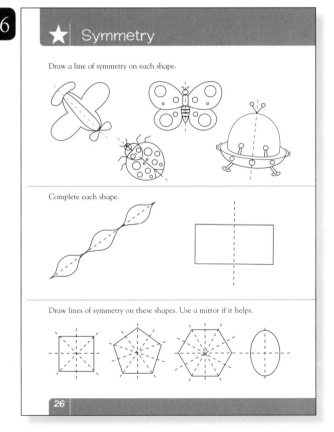

Draw a line of symmetry on each shape.

Complete each shape.

Draw lines of symmetry on these shapes. Use a mirror if it helps.

Encourage children to turn the page at different angles and try to spot as many lines of symmetry as possible rather than to become used to thinking most shapes just have one or two.

2-D shapes ★

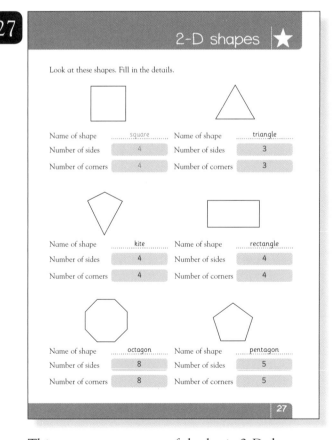

Look at these shapes. Fill in the details.

Name of shape square
Number of sides 4
Number of corners 4

Name of shape triangle
Number of sides 3
Number of corners 3

Name of shape kite
Number of sides 4
Number of corners 4

Name of shape rectangle
Number of sides 4
Number of corners 4

Name of shape octagon
Number of sides 8
Number of corners 8

Name of shape pentagon
Number of sides 5
Number of corners 5

This page covers many of the basic 2-D shapes children will work with at the primary level.

★ 3-D shapes

Look at the shapes. Fill in the details.

Name of shape — cube	Name of shape — sphere
Number of edges — 12	Number of edges — 0
Number of vertices (corners) — 8	Number of vertices (corners) — 0
Name of shape — cuboid	Name of shape — cone
Number of edges — 12	Number of edges — 1
Number of vertices (corners) — 8	Number of vertices (corners) — 1
Name of shape — triangular-based pyramid	Name of shape — cylinder
Number of edges — 6	Number of edges — 2
Number of vertices (corners) — 4	Number of vertices (corners) — 0

This page includes many of the simpler 3-D shapes. Be aware that 2-D shapes have sides, 3-D shapes have edges (a place where two surfaces or faces meet), 2-D shapes have corners, and 3-D shapes have vertex (vertices).

Measurement problems ★

Amy wants to measure the length of her bed using a 30-cm ruler. About how many rulers-long do you think Amy's bed will be?

about 6 rulers

This measuring jug holds 1 litre of water. How many jugs will be needed to fill a bowl that can take 5 litres?

1 litre

5 jugs

Pat has to measure the length of the garden. Circle the best item to use.

tape measure

click wheel

ruler

One apple weighs about 200 g.

Estimate how much two apples will weigh.

400 g

Estimate how much three apples will weigh.

600 g

Children should know about simple measuring tools and when it is appropriate to use one or another.

★ Keeping skills sharp

Jenny is going to a party at 5 o'clock. This is the time now. How many minutes must Jenny wait?

45 minutes

Put these numbers in the correct place.
8   12   14   9   4   18   21

	Odd numbers	Even numbers
Less than 10	9	4 8
More than 10	21	12 14 18

Look at this table.

	Class 3	Class 4	Class 5	Class 6
Boys	15	16	12	14
Girls	16	14	17	17

Which two classes have the same number of children? Class 3 and Class 6

In how many classes are there more girls than boys? 3 classes

Complete this picture to make the house symmetric.

This test covers most of the previous pages and you should be looking to check both your child's accuracy and speed. Accuracy is the priority but speed will indicate the depth of understanding.

Keeping skills sharp ★

Look at these shapes.

Danni says all the shapes have straight sides. Is she right?   no

Fiona says the shapes all have four angles. Is she right?   no

Look at these shapes. Name each shape.

cone   cylinder   cube

Which shape has no curved faces?   cube

Which shape has only two flat faces?   cylinder

Which unit of measurement is correct for the height of a giraffe?   700 centimetres

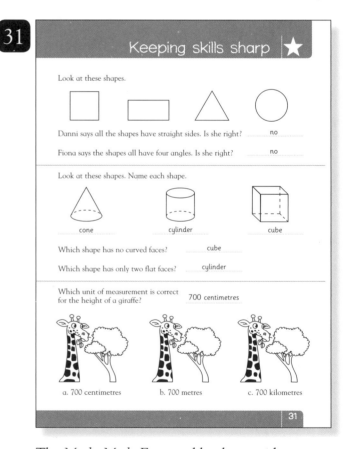

a. 700 centimetres   b. 700 metres   c. 700 kilometres

The *Maths Made Easy* workbooks provide more practice pages.